The Joy of Knowing

A 6-Lesson Study
with Daily Questions

by

Nancy J. Collins

JOY OF LIVING
BIBLE STUDIES

Published by **Joy of Living Bible Studies**

For a free catalog please contact us at:

800-999-2703 or 805-650-0838
info@joyofliving.org • www.joyofliving.org

ISBN   1-932017-66-6

          978-1-932017-66-3

About Joy of Living

For over 40 years Joy of Living has been effectively establishing individuals around the world in the sound, basic study of God's Word.

Evangelical and interdenominational, Joy of Living reaches across denominational and cultural barriers, enriching lives through the simple, pure truths of God's inspired Word, the Bible.

Our goal is...

To help people enter into a joyous, intimate relationship with God the Father, as they come to know His Son, Jesus Christ, as Lord and Savior.

To help believers discover the fulfillment and joy that comes from daily Bible study and personal devotional time with the Lord.

To enrich lives by helping people know, understand, and apply to their lives the truths in God's inspired Word, the Bible.

To help believers grow in the grace and knowledge of our Lord and Savior Jesus Christ, so that they may please Him in every way, and experience the abundant life He has promised to His people.

To build confidence and enthusiasm in believers for sharing their faith and the joy of knowing the Lord with others.

To provide Bible study materials, at a reasonable cost, to those desiring to study God's Word, and to those desiring to teach the truth of God's Word to others.

Table of Contents

About Joy of Living 2

Do You KNOW You Have Eternal Life? 4

How to Use This Study 5

A Good Place to Start.. 6

Lesson 1 — The Bible 7

Lesson 2 — God 21

Lesson 3 — The Trinity 35

Lesson 4 — The Human Race 49

Lesson 5 — Sin, Death, Life.. 63

Lesson 6 — Knowing 77

How much better to get wisdom than gold, to choose understanding rather than silver!
Proverbs 16:16

Do You KNOW You Have Eternal Life?

Your Condition...

For all have sinned and fall short of the glory of God. (Romans 3:23)

But your iniquities (sins) have separated you from your God. (Isaiah 59:2)

For the wages of sin is death. (Romans 6:23)

There is help...

For Christ died for sins once for all, the righteous for the unrighteous, to bring you to God. (1 Peter 3:18)

The gift of God is eternal life in Christ Jesus our Lord. (Romans 6:23)

What do I do?...

Repent, then, and turn to God, so that your sins may be wiped out. (Acts 3:19)

Believe in the Lord Jesus, and you will be saved. (Acts 16:31)

You CAN know...

He who has the Son has life; he who does not have the Son of God does not have life. I write these things to you who believe in the name of the Son of God so that you may know that you have eternal life. (1 John 5:12-13)

If you would like to make the decision today to repent and trust Christ as your Savior, either for the first time or as a re-commitment of your life, you may want to pray a prayer similar to this one:

Lord Jesus, I admit that I am a sinner. Please forgive my sins. Thank You for dying on the cross for me, and for coming alive again. I accept Your gifts of forgiveness and eternal life. I place my life in Your hands. I want to be Yours forever. Thank you for loving me so much.

In Your Name I pray,
Amen

How to Use This Study

Only a Bible is needed for this study.

- · The Bible verses referenced each day are listed for your convenience on the right hand side of the second page of each lesson day. When possible, we suggest you read the verses in their entirety in your own Bible.
- · The additional reading at the bottom of that same page is not part of the daily study, but has been provided for those who want to explore the subject more thoroughly.

As you work through each lesson, it is important to allow the Holy Spirit to reveal God's truth to you and to help you apply it to your own life and circumstances. If desired, you may consult additional commentaries after answering the questions in the lesson.

We strongly suggest that you work through the weekly lesson on a consistent daily basis rather than attempting to complete an entire lesson at one time. As you work through each daily lesson, pray and ask God to help you know, understand, and apply His truth to your life.

Remember, the point of Bible study is to know God and to build your relationship with Him.

To Use in a Group Setting:

After the daily personal study questions have been completed, the students gather in a small group, where they pray together and discuss what they have written in response to the questions, clarifying problem areas and gaining more insight into what was studied. The small group/discussion leader helps the group focus on biblical truth, and not just on personal problems. The student is the only person who sees their own answers and shares only what they feel comfortable sharing.

After small groups meet for discussion and prayer, they often gather in a large group meeting where a teacher gives a brief lecture covering the essential teaching of what was studied during the prior week and discussed in the small groups. The teacher may clarify what was studied and challenge class members to live a more committed daily life.

At home, the student begins the next lesson, reading the Bible passages and answering the questions.

A Good Place to Start...

We often hear the question, "What study should I do first? Where in the Bible should I start?"

Second Timothy 3:16 states, "All Scripture is God-breathed and is useful for teaching, rebuking, correcting and training in righteousness." There is no "bad" place to begin, because the Holy Spirit can and will use any portion of Scripture1 to accomplish His purpose (see Isaiah 55:10-11). There are, however, some truths and starting points that may make studying the Bible easier.

Whether you are opening the Word of God for the first time, or you've been studying for many years, we hope that this study will deepen your understanding of God and His Word and lay a foundation that will enrich your continued study.

Many of the truths that are presented in this study may not be new to you. However if you will take the time to work through the lessons, we believe you will develop a greater understanding that will enable you to confidently share your faith with others, and help you develop a pattern of daily study.

Make a daily appointment with God. Find a quiet spot. Take your Bible and this study with you. If you have a busy phone, mute it or turn it off! Remember how very important your appointment with God is, and make time to be with Him daily. Ask yourself the following things:

How much time will I spend with the Lord each day?

What do I need to put aside in order to spend this time with the Lord? (Examples: texting, TV, digital games, etc.) Each person will have to decide what his or her priorities are and what can be removed from the daily schedule to make time to spend with God.

What is the best time for my appointment with God?

Where is the quietest place for me to pray and study?

Do I really want to spend time with God? If you do, He will help you find the time.

---

1 The terms "Bible", "Word of God", and "Scripture" are used interchangeably in this study.

Lesson 1 — The Bible

- How is the Bible different from other books?
- Is it reliable?
- Is it relevant for today?
- How will it benefit me?

Remember, as you work through each daily lesson, pray and ask God to help you know, understand, and apply His truth to your life.

The Bible - Day One

Read: Psalm 119:89 • 2 Timothy 3:16a • 2 Peter 1:21

Many of humanity's questions are summed up in the single word, "Why?"

God has the answers to those questions, and He is willing to reveal most of the answers to us, *if* we truly want to know those answers and then act upon the truth those answers reveal.

The answers are not usually simple answers. It's possible your world view and the entire way you think may be changed, in order to receive and understand God's answers.

Where do we go to get God's answers? To God, to His Word, His book—the Bible.

The Bible is like no other book. It was written by over 40 authors from various backgrounds, over a period of about 1,600 years—in complete harmony. For this number of people, from different walks of life, in different periods of time, to write in complete harmony is a miracle.

• **From** today's Bible verses (printed on the right side of the next page), what does the Bible say about itself?

• **Based** on these Bible verses, how reliable is God's Word?

Generation after generation there have been many who have attacked the Bible...without success. John Clifford wrote a poem about this:

The Anvil of God's Word

Last eve I passed beside a blacksmith's door
And heard the anvil ring the vesper chime;
When looking in, I saw upon the floor,
Old hammers worn with beating years of time.

Today's Bible Reading

"How many anvils have you had," said I,
"To wear and batter these hammers so?"
"Just one," said he; then with a twinkling eye,
"The anvil wears the hammers out, you know."

And so, I thought, the anvil of God's Word,
For ages, skeptics blows have beat upon;
Yet, though the noise of falling blows was heard,
The anvil is unharmed—the hammers gone.

Your word, LORD, is eternal; it stands firm in the heavens.
— Psalm 119:89

All Scripture is God-breathed...
— 2 Timothy 3:16a

For prophecy never had its origin in the human will, but prophets, though human, spoke from God as they were carried along by the Holy Spirit.
— 2 Peter 1:21

Have you been the type of person who picks and chooses what you prefer to believe? God does not give us that option. Either we believe what He says is true or we don't.

- **Perhaps** you have doubts. Ask God to show you His truth as you continue in this study. *If you truly want to know in order to obey the truth, He will show you (see John 7:17).*

- **Do** you already know His Word is true? Ask God to deepen your understanding and enrich your relationship with Him as you continue with this study.

Additional reading:
2 Samuel 23:2
Psalm 119:160
Matthew 24:35
1 Peter 1:25
Isaiah 40:8
John 7:17

The Bible - Day Two

Read: 1 Corinthians 2:14 • John 3:3 • John 1:12-13

You may ask, "Can I personally understand what God says and means in the Bible? After all, there are a lot of interpretations and opinions regarding what the Bible has to say." God has an answer for you!

• **From** 1 Corinthians 2:14, why are some people unable to understand God's truth?

• **From** John 3:3, what must happen before a person can see, or perceive, the kingdom of God?

Stop a moment and consider the following. Can a bird understand a person's thoughts, hopes, dreams, concerns, and plans—in other words, what a person thinks and feels? Of course not. The only way a bird could understand is if it could somehow have a human spirit—be born all over again as a human being. And so we humans cannot understand the things of God unless we are born all over again by God's Spirit, and thus become His child.

• **From** John 1:12-13 what must a person do to be born of God?

- **Have** you been born of God's Spirit? If not, and you want to be:

a. Decide that you want to go God's way instead of your own. (This is *repentance*.)

b. Acknowledge to God that you are a sinner.

c. Receive Jesus as your Savior. This means that you believe that Jesus Christ is the Son of God, that His death on the cross paid the price for your sin, that He rose from the dead, and that you want Him to be the Lord of your life.

This is the starting point of knowing and understanding God. You may turn to page 4 for additional information on the new birth and eternal life.

- **When** were you born again by God's Spirit?

Today's Bible Reading

The person without the Spirit does not accept the things that come from the Spirit of God but considers them foolishness, and cannot understand them because they are discerned only through the Spirit.

— 1 Corinthians 2:14

Jesus replied, "Very truly I tell you, no one can see the kingdom of God unless they are born again."

— John 3:3

Yet to all who did receive him, to those who believed in his name, he gave the right to become children of God — children born not of natural descent, nor of human decision or a husband's will, but born of God.

— John 1:12-13

Additional reading:
John 3:4-6
1 Peter 1:3
1 Peter 1:23

The Bible - Day Three

Read: 1 Peter 2:2 • 2 Peter 1:3 • 2 Peter 3:18a

The Word of God plays a critical part in our spiritual birth.[1] It is by God's Word that we are given the faith to believe, and through His Word we are born of God's Spirit (see 1 Peter 1:23; Romans 10:17).

After our rebirth, God's Word continues to be vital to our lives. One major role it plays is as nourishment for the believer. From Hebrews 5:12 we learn that God's Word serves as both milk for the young in Christ and meat for the more mature Christian.

- **From** 1 Peter 2:2, how eager should we be for God's Word and what will it do for us?

God has given us a brand new life, and He intends for it to be an abundant life filled with love, joy, peace, and so much more (see John 10:10; Galatians 5:22-23). Unfortunately, many Christians don't experience this abundant life because they fail to grow up (become mature) in Christ.

- **Look** at 2 Peter 1:3. Through what means has God provided all that we need for this new life?

- **According** to 2 Peter 3:18a, in what areas are we to grow?

This new abundant life that we live is centered in knowing God and having an intimate relationship with Him. John 17:3 says, "Now this is eternal life: that they may know you, the only true God, and Jesus Christ, whom you have sent."

It is primarily through our words that we communicate who we are, our feelings, thoughts, intentions, desires—our very essence. And so it is with God. He communicates to us primarily through His Word, the Bible. In it He reveals to us His thoughts, intentions, desires—who He is.

We, who were dead in our sin and enemies of God, were reconciled to Him by the death of His Son, Jesus Christ. Consider to what great lengths God has gone, in order that we can know Him and have a relationship with Him.

[1] Being born of God's Spirit is sometimes referred to as being "born again" or being "saved."

- **Have** you really thought about this—that the Creator of the Universe desires a relationship with you? How do you feel about this?

A newborn has very little interpersonal relationship with anyone, even its mother. Its focus is on its needs. As the infant begins to grow, it begins to recognize people, faces, and voices. It smiles and coos, as well as cries, as it begins to learn to communicate. The infant begins to enjoy sights, sounds and discovery, but understands very little about the world around it. A young child knows more about his or her parents and can communicate, but on an immature level. That child understands more about living and enjoying the life he or she was born with. The son or daughter who has reached adulthood is able to enjoy mature relationships with the parents. He or she understands how the world functions and experiences life more completely.

- **We** can compare our spiritual life to this type of growth. Where are you on the list: A newborn crying for its needs to be met— always, "I want… I need… Give me…"? A toddler beginning to communicate, learning self-control, and enjoying the challenge of discovery? A youth taking pleasure in all that you are able to do, capable of conveying your thoughts and feelings, and able to understand and reason? An adult beginning to savor the rich fellowship that only maturity and understanding can bring?

- **Do** you want all that God has for you—the deep, mature, abundant life that springs from a close, intimate relationship with Him?

Today's Bible Reading

Like newborn babies, crave pure spiritual milk, so that by it you may grow up in your salvation.

— 1 Peter 2:2

His divine power has given us everything we need for a godly life through our knowledge of him who called us by his own glory and goodness.

— 2 Peter 1:3

But grow in the grace and knowledge of our Lord and Savior Jesus Christ.

— 2 Peter 3:18a

Additional reading:
1 Peter 1:23
Romans 10:17
Hebrews 5:12
John 10:10
Galatians 5:22-23

The Bible - Day Four

Read: 2 Timothy 3:16-17 • Ephesians 2:10 • Hebrews 4:12

The Bible is like no other book. We have seen the vital role the Word of God plays in our spiritual birth and growth.

• **Looking** at 2 Timothy 3:16-17, for what else is Scripture useful? And to what purpose or end?

Just as God intended for the first man, Adam, to find fulfillment by tending the Garden of Eden (prior to the fall, see Genesis 2:15), so God intends us to find fulfillment in the work that He has given us to do.

• **From** Ephesians 2:10, after we have been born of God's Spirit, what does God have planned for us to do?

As Scripture so plainly tells us, these are not works we do in order to be saved (see Ephesians 2:8-9). These good works are part of the abundant life God has for us to enjoy. The good works that bring joy and satisfaction are those that spring forth from the new life within us—out of the love that God has put into our hearts (see Romans 5:5).

God uses His Word in our lives to bring us into maturity and to prepare us for all that He has for us to do. As young believers (or older believers who have not matured in God's Word), we often rush about attempting to do good deeds, seeking to serve the Lord in ways for which we are not prepared and from motives that may be less than pure—motives that we may not realize lie behind our actions.

- **From** Hebrews 4:12, how will the Word of God help us in this area—regardless of how long we have been a Christian?

- **Name** at least one specific time that God has used His Word to correct your thinking, convict you of sin, rebuke you, or cut right through everything to show you what your motives really were.

Today's Bible Reading

All Scripture is God-breathed and is useful for teaching, rebuking, correcting and training in righteousness, so that the servant of God may be thoroughly equipped for every good work.

— 2 Timothy 3:16-17

For we are God's handiwork, created in Christ Jesus to do good works, which God prepared in advance for us to do.

— Ephesians 2:10

For the word of God is alive and active. Sharper than any double-edged sword, it penetrates even to dividing soul and spirit, joints and marrow; it judges the thoughts and attitudes of the heart.

— Hebrews 4:12

Additional reading:
Genesis 2:15
Ephesians 2:8-9
Romans 5:5

The Bible - Day Five

Read: Luke 12:19 • Luke 12:20-21 • 2 Timothy 2:15

God's message is the same from Genesis to Revelation. He does not contradict Himself. However, what someone has said can be misunderstood by taking it out of context. And so it is with God's Word. If taken out of context, a Bible verse may seem to say something that it does not.

- **Read** only Luke 12:19 and, without considering the context, write what it appears to be saying.

- **Now** read Luke 12:19 with the two verses that follow (Luke 12:20-21). How do these verses entirely change what it seems Luke 12:19, by itself, means?[1]

As you read, it is important to read in context and to consider:

· Who is speaking and to whom are they speaking?

· Why they are saying what they are saying—are they endeavoring to make a point?

---

[1] You will get a more complete understanding of this passage if you read the entire story in Luke 12:15-22.

· What do the words really mean? If you come to a word you don't use very often, you may think you know what it means, but try looking it up in the dictionary. You may be surprised at what you learn. Knowing the full meaning of a word often broadens and sometimes changes our understanding of a verse or passage.

If you are serious about your relationship with the Lord, you will be serious about what He is saying to you. You will take the time to understand, and not just assume you know what He is saying.

· **What** does 2 Timothy 2:15 encourage you to do?

Today's Bible Reading

And I'll say to myself, "You have plenty of grain laid up for many years. Take life easy; eat, drink and be merry."

— Luke 12:19

But God said to him, "You fool! This very night your life will be demanded from you. Then who will get what you have prepared for yourself? This is how it will be with whoever stores up things for themselves but is not rich towards God."

— Luke 12:20-21

Do your best to present yourself to God as one approved, a worker who does not need to be ashamed and who correctly handles the word of truth.

— 2 Timothy 2:15

Additional reading:
Luke 12:15-22

The Bible - Day Six

Read: Psalm 119:11 • Psalm 119:105 • Psalm 19:7 • Acts 17:11

Along with helping us build our relationship with the Lord, there are so many benefits to knowing God's Word. Today, let us look for a few.

• **In** Psalm 119:11, why did the psalmist hide God's Word in his heart?

God's Word teaches what is right and wrong, and it strengthens us spiritually so that we can choose to do what is right.

• **Sometimes** our path through life seems dark and difficult, with danger everywhere, and we don't know what direction to take. Look at Psalm 119:105 and write what benefit there is to knowing God's Word.

• **We** have all probably experienced one of those days, or even periods of time, when so much has happened or is happening that we are just plain weary—emotionally drained. Look at Psalm 19:7a. What will God's Word do? Have you ever experienced this?

Today's Bible Reading

• **Perhaps** you know a lot about computers, or science, or teaching, but when it comes to making life choices you just don't seem to have much wisdom—your choices are often the wrong choices. What hope does Psalm 19:7b give to you?

I have hidden your word in my heart that I might not sin against you.
— Psalm 119:11

Your word is a lamp for my feet, a light on my path.
— Psalm 119:105

The law of the LORD is perfect, refreshing the soul.
— Psalm 19:7a

The statutes of the LORD are trustworthy, making wise the simple.
— Psalm 19:7b

Throughout both the Old and New Testaments we are warned about false teachers. Jesus refers to them as wolves in sheep's clothing (see Matthew 7:15). The Apostle Paul says they are "full of deception" (Titus 1:10). The Apostle John warns us that many false prophets have gone out into the world (see 1 John 4:1).

Now the Berean Jews were of more noble character than those in Thessalonica, for they received the message with great eagerness and examined the Scriptures every day to see if what Paul said was true.
— Acts 17:11

• **From** Acts 17:11, what did the Bereans do when they first heard what the Apostle Paul was preaching?

Additional reading:
Matthew 4:4
Matthew 7:15
Titus 1:10
1 John 4:1
1 John 2:1-16
Hebrews 4:12

The Bible - Day Seven

Take a few minutes today to re-read the Bible verses from this week. Write down what has been most meaningful to you.

As you have worked through the study this week, we hope that you have discovered how very important God's Word is and that you have made a new commitment to read and study the Bible.

Lesson 2 — God

·   Is there a God?

·   What's He like?

·   Does He care?

·   Does He matter?

Remember, as you work through each daily lesson, pray and ask God to help you know, understand, and apply His truth to your life.

God - Day One

Read: Romans 1:20 • Jeremiah 10:10a • Isaiah 45:18 • Acts 7:32a

The opening verse of the Bible states, "In the beginning God..." (Genesis 1:1). The Bible does not argue the fact that God exists; instead it states that only a fool says that there is no God (see Psalm 53:1).

- **From** Romans 1:20, what do you learn about God's revelation to people[1] and why only a fool would say there is no God?

- **What** do you learn about God from Jeremiah 10:10a?

- **There** are those who believe there are many gods. What does the One who created the heavens and the earth say about Himself in Isaiah 45:18?

---

[1] Psalm 19:1-4 also speaks of God's revelation of Himself through nature.

Some people believe that there is just one god and that he goes by different names in different religions. God says otherwise. He tells us very specifically who He is.

• **From** Acts 7:32, who, specifically, is God?

Throughout the Bible, God reveals Himself to us. As you read and study God's Word, you come to understand that there is only one true and living God, Creator of heaven and earth. He is the God of Abraham, Isaac, and Jacob, and He sent His Son, Jesus Christ, to be the Savior of the world.

Today's Bible Reading

For since the creation of the world God's invisible qualities—his eternal power and divine nature—have been clearly seen, being understood from what has been made, so that people are without excuse.

— Romans 1:20

But the LORD is the true God; he is the living God, the eternal King.

— Jeremiah 10:10a

For this is what the LORD says—he who created the heavens, he is God; he who fashioned and made the earth, he founded it; he did not create it to be empty, but formed it to be inhabited—he says: "I am the LORD, and there is no other."

— Isaiah 45:18

I am the God of your fathers, the God of Abraham, Isaac and Jacob.

— Acts 7:32a

Additional reading:
Genesis 1:1
Psalm 53:1
Psalm 19:1-4

God - Day Two

Read: John 3:16a • Proverbs 6:16 • Genesis 6:6 • Numbers 22:22a •
1 Peter 5:6-7 • Zephaniah 3:17

God is not merely a force; He is a person, and we are created in His
image.

- **What** feelings does God show in each of the following verses that
  indicate that He is a person and not just a force?

  · John 3:16a

  · Proverbs 6:16

  · Genesis 6:6

  · Numbers 22:22a

  · 1 Peter 5:6-7

  · Zephaniah 3:17

- **Consider** this for a moment. Have you ever considered God's feelings before?

- **How** does knowing that God is a person with emotions change your perception of Him?

- **Does** this change your feelings toward Him?

Today's Bible Reading

For God so loved the world…
— John 3:16a

There are six things the LORD hates, seven that are detestable to him.
— Proverbs 6:16

The Lord regretted that he had made human beings on the earth, and his heart was deeply troubled.
— Genesis 6:6

But God was very angry when he went…
— Numbers 22:22a

Humble yourselves, therefore, under God's mighty hand, that he may lift you up in due time. Cast all your anxiety on him because he cares for you.
— 1 Peter 5: 6-7

The Lord your God is with you, the Mighty Warrior who saves. He will take great delight in you; in his love he will no longer rebuke you, but will rejoice over you with singing.
— Zephaniah 3:17

Additional reading:
Genesis 1:27

God - Day Three

Read: Deuteronomy 4:31a • Deuteronomy 7:9a • Deuteronomy 10:17 • Psalm 99:9b • John 4:24b • 1 John 1:5b • 1 John 4:8b

The term we use to describe the fundamental qualities of a person, their essential character, is their *nature*.

- **From** the following verses write what you learn about God's nature:
  - Deuteronomy 4:31a

  - Deuteronomy 7:9a

  - Deuteronomy 10:17

  - Psalm 99:9b

  - John 4:24b

· 1 John 1:5b

· 1 John 4:8b

· **Look** back through the list you have just written that describes God's nature. How does this change the way you view God?

· **Is** this the type of person you would like to know?

Today's Bible Reading

For the LORD your God is a merciful God…
— Deuteronomy 4:31a

Know therefore that the LORD your God is God; he is the faithful God…
— Deuteronomy 7:9a

For the LORD your God is God of gods and Lord of lords, the great God, mighty and awesome, who shows no partiality and accepts no bribes.
— Deuteronomy 10:17

…for the LORD our God is holy.
— Psalm 99:9b

God is spirit…
— John 4:24b

God is light; in him there is no darkness at all.
— 1 John 1:5b

…God is love.
— 1 John 4:8b

God - Day Four

Read: Psalm 139:7-10 • Psalm 147:5 • Jeremiah 32:17 • John 5:26 • Revelation 19:6

Although Job 36:26 tells us that God is so great that we can't fully understand Him, and that all the descriptions we have read about Him are incomplete, we have discovered that there are many things we *can* know about Him.

• **From** the following verses, what do you learn about how great God is?

· Psalm 139:7-10

· Psalm 147:5

· Jeremiah 32:17

· John 5:26

· Revelation 19:6

Just consider this, God is almighty (omnipotent)—He even has life within himself; He is all knowing (omniscient); and He is everywhere present (omnipresent). That alone should make one tremble with fear.

But this great and mighty God loves us and has gone to great lengths on our behalf.

- **Write** briefly how this makes you feel.

Today's Bible Reading

Where can I go from your Spirit? Where can I flee from your presence? If I go up to the heavens, you are there; if I make my bed in the depths, you are there. If I rise on the wings of the dawn, if I settle on the far side of the sea, even there your hand will guide me, your right hand will hold me fast.

— Psalm 139:7-10

Great is our Lord and mighty in power; his understanding has no limit.

— Psalm 147:5

Ah, Sovereign LORD, you have made the heavens and the earth by your great power and outstretched arm. Nothing is too hard for you.

— Jeremiah 32:17

For as the Father has life in himself, so he has granted the Son also to have life in himself.

— John 5:26

Then I heard what sounded like a great multitude, like the roar of rushing waters and like loud peals of thunder, shouting: "Hallelujah! For our Lord God Almighty reigns."

— Revelation 19:6

Additional reading:
Job 36:26

God - Day Five

Read: Mark 12:29 • 1 Peter 1:2a • Hebrews 1:8 • Acts 5:3a,4b •
Matthew 3:16-17 • Matthew 28:19

Today we will look at some other aspects of God. It is important to
remember that the Bible does not contradict itself.

• **What** do you learn about God from Mark 12:29?

• **How** is God referred to in 1 Peter 1:2a?

• **Hebrews** 1:8 speaks of Jesus Christ as "the Son." By what name is He
referred to in this passage?

• **A story** is told in Acts 5 about a couple who sold some land and
pretended to give all the money to the Lord's work, although they actually
kept some for themselves. The problem wasn't that they had kept some
of the money, but that they had lied about it. Look at Acts 5:3a,4b. To
whom did they lie? By what name is He called in this passage?

• **Matthew** 3:16-17 took place at the Jordan River when Jesus was
baptized. Read through this passage and write down what three persons
are referred to.

Scripture does not contradict itself. God is beyond our complete understanding because He is infinite and we are finite, limited beings. God is described as Father, Son, and Holy Spirit, yet He is one. The terms we use to describe this are the "Trinity" or the "Godhead." These words themselves are not used in the Bible.

- **From** Matthew 28:19, whose name (not "names") are we to baptize in?

In attempting to explain how there can be three, yet one, all we have to do is look at ourselves. We consist of body, soul, and spirit[1] in one person (see 1 Thessalonians 5:23). Time consists of past, present, and future. There are other examples, but everything falls short when we attempt to explain the infinite God.

- **What** are your thoughts about this?

Today's Bible Reading

"The most important one," answered Jesus, *"is this: 'Hear, O Israel: The Lord our God, the Lord is one.'"*
— Mark 12:29

...who have been chosen according to the foreknowledge of God the Father...
— 1 Peter 1:2a

But about the Son he says, "Your throne, O God, will last for ever and ever; a scepter of justice will be the scepter of your kingdom."
— Hebrews 1:8

Then Peter said, "Ananias, how is it that Satan has so filled your heart that you have lied to the Holy Spirit...You have not lied just to human beings but to God."
— Acts 5:3a,4b

As soon as Jesus was baptized, he went up out of the water. At that moment heaven was opened, and he saw the Spirit of God descending like a dove and alighting on him. And a voice from heaven said, "This is my Son, whom I love; with him I am well pleased."
— Matthew 3:16-17

Therefore go and make disciples of all nations, baptizing them in the name of the Father and of the Son and of the Holy Spirit.
— Matthew 28:19

---

[1] "Soul" is that invisible dimension of our life that we are by nature (for example, our emotions, personality, mind, and will). "Spirit" is what we are by supernatural rebirth. Jesus said, "Flesh gives birth to flesh, but the Spirit gives birth to spirit" (John 3:6).

Additional reading:
1 Thessalonians 5:23
John 1:1-4,14

God - Day Six

Read: Ephesians 2:8 • John 3:16 • Revelation 22:17 • Titus 2:11-12 •
2 Corinthians 12:9a

There is another aspect of God that we will look at. It is His grace.
According to Merriam-Webster's online dictionary, *grace* is "unmerited
divine assistance given humans." Nehemiah 9:31 tells us that God is
gracious and merciful.

• **From** Ephesians 2:8, how does one obtain or become the recipient of
God's grace?

In Romans 3:23-24 we learn that all people (including you and I) have
sinned, and they don't measure up to God's standard, which is perfection.
Yet we also read that God has justified us freely— declared us not guilty.
He did this through Jesus Christ, who took away our sin. This is called
grace.

• **Read** John 3:16 and Revelation 22:17. Who is invited to receive God's
grace?

• **Have** you accepted God's grace by receiving Jesus Christ as your
Savior? Remember, you cannot earn and you do not deserve God's
grace and forgiveness. Will you accept this gift from God today?

- **God's** grace is extended to us so that our sins might be forgiven, and it is there to help us live the type of life that pleases God. What do you learn about this from Titus 2:11-12?

- **God's** grace is available to us in every situation we face. What do you learn about His grace in 2 Corinthians 12:9a?

God's grace is sufficient—it is enough. He has saved us by His grace. His grace helps us live the kind of life that pleases Him and satisfies us. And His grace is there for whatever may come our way. Take a moment now and thank Him.

Today's Bible Reading

For it is by grace you have been saved, through faith—and this is not from yourselves, it is the gift of God…

— Ephesians 2:8

For God so loved the world that he gave his one and only Son, that whoever believes in him shall not perish but have eternal life.

— John 3:16

The Spirit and the bride say, "Come!" And let the one who hears say, "Come!" Let the one who is thirsty come; and let the one who wishes take the free gift of the water of life.

— Revelation 22:17

For the grace of God has appeared that offers salvation to all people. It teaches us to say "No" to ungodliness and worldly passions, and to live self-controlled, upright and godly lives in this present age.

— Titus 2:11-12

But he said to me, "My grace is sufficient for you…"

— 2 Corinthians 12:9a

Additional reading:
Nehemiah 9:31
Romans 3:23-24
Ephesians 1:7

God - Day Seven

Take a few minutes today to re-read the Bible verses from this week. Write down what has been most meaningful to you.

As you have worked through the study this week, we hope that you have come to a deeper understanding of God and that you have a new desire to know Him better.

Lesson 3 — The Trinity

- One God? OK...
- Father?
- Son?
- Holy Spirit?

Remember, as you work through each daily lesson, pray and ask God to help you know, understand, and apply His truth to your life.

The Trinity - Day One

Read: John 3:16 • Romans 5:8 • Psalm 139:1-4

In the previous lesson we learned many facts about God. This week we will take a closer look at the individual members of the Trinity—the Father, the Son, and the Holy Spirit.

Many people have misconceptions about God the Father. Their view is often a mixture of various thoughts and teachings that they've combined in their minds, rather than what He has revealed about Himself in the Scriptures.

• **According** to John 3:16, how does God feel about the human race?

• **Love** is more than just a word or a feeling. Love moves us to do something for the one who is loved. Read Romans 5:8. When and how did God demonstrate (show) His love for humanity?

- **You** may read through these passages and think that God loves and sent His Son to die for the world in general, but that when it comes to you as an individual, He may not be interested in you. Read Psalm 139:1-4, and write down how intimately God knows you and is concerned about you as an individual.

- **It** is amazing to consider that God loves you and me as individuals, and that He knows us intimately and is concerned about the smallest details of our lives—He even knows the number of hairs we have on our heads (see Matthew 10:30). What do you think and feel about this?

Today's Bible Reading

For God so loved the world that he gave his one and only Son, that whoever believes in him shall not perish but have eternal life.

— John 3:16

But God demonstrates his own love for us in this: While we were still sinners, Christ died for us.

— Romans 5:8

You have searched me, LORD, and you know me. You know when I sit and when I rise; you perceive my thoughts from afar. You discern my going out and my lying down; you are familiar with all my ways. Before a word is on my tongue, you, LORD, know it completely.

— Psalm 139:1-4

Additional reading:
Matthew 10:30
1 John 4:14

The Trinity - Day Two

Read: John 3:35 • John 5:20 • John 14:6 • Matthew 11:27b

God the Father has a special relationship with and to God the Son.

- **Read** John 3:35 and John 5:20. Describe the special relationship between the Father and the Son.

- **Some** people believe that they can have a relationship with the Father without becoming a Christian (i.e. without accepting Christ as their Savior). What does John 14:6 say regarding this?

- **What** does Matthew 11:27b tell us about who knows the Father?

Acts 10 tells of a Roman centurion named Cornelius. "He and all his family were devout and God-fearing; he gave generously to those in need and prayed to God regularly" (verse 2). God heard Cornelius' prayers and saw his actions (see verse 31). The Lord sent an angel to tell Cornelius to send for the Apostle Peter, and to listen to what he had to say.

Cornelius obeyed. When Peter arrived, he explained to Cornelius about Jesus—how He died to pay the price for our sin so that we could have a relationship with God, and that He rose again from the dead. Cornelius, his family, and all those with them believed and were baptized that very day.

Perhaps you've been one of those who have tried to be devout and God-fearing like Cornelius. Just as He sent Peter to Cornelius, God has sent this study to you, in order that you might put your faith and trust in Jesus Christ to take away your sin and bring you into a relationship with God.

- **If** you haven't, won't you put your faith in Him today? See page 4 for more information.

Today's Bible Reading

The Father loves the Son and has placed everything in his hands.
— John 3:35

For the Father loves the Son and shows him all he does.
— John 5:20

Jesus answered, "I am the way and the truth and the life. No one comes to the Father except through me."
— John 14:6

No one knows the Son except the Father, and no one knows the Father except the Son and those to whom the Son chooses to reveal him.
— Matthew 11:27b

Additional reading:
Acts 10
John 6:45
2 John 1:9

The Trinity - Day Three

Read: John 1:1b • John 20:28 • Hebrews 1:8a • John 1:3 •
Colossians 1:15-17

When asked what they believe about Jesus, people have a variety of answers. Some say they believe He was merely a good man; others say He was a prophet; some believe He is God.

• **Before** proceeding, consider what you think about Jesus Christ, His character, who He is, etc.

We will now explore Scripture and see how correct you have been.

• **We** are told in John 1:14 that Jesus Christ is "the Word." How is He referred to in John 1:1b, John 20:28, and Hebrews 1:8?

• **John** 1:3 speaks of the Word (Jesus Christ). What do you learn about Him from this verse?

- **Colossians** 1:15-17 also refers to Jesus Christ. What do you learn about Him from these verses?

...and the Word was God.
— John 1:1b

Thomas said to him, "My Lord and my God!"
— John 20:28

But about the Son he says, "Your throne, O God, will last for ever and ever."
— Hebrews 1:8a

Through him all things were made; without him nothing was made that has been made.
—John 1:3

- **As** you can see from the Bible, Jesus is so much more than just a good man, a great teacher, or a prophet. Is any of this information new to you? What difference does this make to you?

The Son is the image of the invisible God, the firstborn over all creation. For in him all things were created: things in heaven and on earth, visible and invisible, whether thrones or powers or rulers or authorities; all things have been created through him and for him. He is before all things, and in him all things hold together
— Colossians 1:15-17

Additional reading:
John 1:14

The Trinity - Day Four

Read: Luke 1:34-35 • Matthew 1:20-25

Jesus didn't just appear in an adult human body. Luke 1:26—2:7 tells of the events surrounding His birth. God sent an angel to a virgin named Mary, to tell her she was going to have a son. This child would be called the Son of the Most High, He would sit on the throne of His father David, and He would reign forever.

- **From** Luke 1:34-35, what was unique about the conception of Jesus?

Joseph, who was engaged to Mary, didn't know what to do when he learned of Mary's pregnancy. He knew he was not the father of this child. Read Matthew 1:20-25.

- **How** did God communicate with Joseph?

- **What** information was given to Joseph about the child?

- **What** prophecies were fulfilled?[1]

- **What** did Joseph do in response to the information given to him in the dream?

- **Joseph** responded in obedience to God's direction through a dream. Will you respond to God's direction to you through His Word, the Bible?

"How will this be," Mary asked the angel, "since I am a virgin?" The angel answered, "The Holy Spirit will come on you, and the power of the Most High will overshadow you. So the holy one to be born will be called the Son of God."

— Luke 1:34-35

But after he had considered this, an angel of the Lord appeared to him in a dream and said, "Joseph son of David, do not be afraid to take Mary home as your wife, because what is conceived in her is from the Holy Spirit. She will give birth to a son, and you are to give him the name Jesus, because he will save his people from their sins." All this took place to fulfill what the Lord had said through the prophet: "The virgin will conceive and give birth to a son, and they will call him Immanuel" (which means "God with us"). When Joseph woke up, he did what the angel of the Lord had commanded him and took Mary home as his wife. But he did not consummate their marriage until she gave birth to a son. And he gave him the name Jesus.

— Matthew 1:20-25

Additional reading:
Luke 1:26—2:7

---

[1]The Old Testament, which was written hundreds of years before Jesus' birth, contains over 300 prophecies that were fulfilled through Jesus' life, death, and resurrection.

The Trinity - Day Five

Read: Luke 2:52a • Matthew 8:24b • Matthew 21:18b • John 4:6b • John 19:28b • Matthew 26:37b • Mark 3:5a • Hebrews 4:15

Jesus Christ is completely God. Knowing this, it is amazing to consider that He became completely human. In yesterday's lesson we saw that He was born of a woman. Today we will see that He experienced all the human limitations and difficulties we experience.

From the following verses, what did Jesus experience that shows He was human?

- Luke 2:52a

- Matthew 8:24b

- Matthew 21:18b

- John 4:6b

- John 19:28b

· Matthew 26:37b

· Mark 3:5a

· **How** does Hebrews 4:15 express Jesus' humanity, and yet show that He was like no other human?

· **Briefly** state what you have learned about Jesus that you didn't know before or hadn't thought much about, and tell what difference this makes to you.

Today's Bible Reading

And Jesus grew in wisdom and stature…
— Luke 2:52a

…Jesus was sleeping.
— Matthew 8:24b

…he was hungry.
— Matthew 21:18b

…and Jesus, tired as he was from the journey…
— John 4: 6b

…Jesus said, "I am thirsty."
— John 19:28b

…he began to be sorrowful and troubled.
— Matthew 26:37b

He looked round at them in anger and, deeply distressed…
— Mark 3:5a

For we do not have a high priest who is unable to empathize with our weaknesses, but we have one who has been tempted in every way, just as we are— yet he did not sin.
— Hebrews 4:15

The Trinity - Day Six

Read: Ephesians 1:13b-14a • Acts 1:8a • Romans 5:5b •
Galatians 5:22-23a • John 16:13-14

Remember, the Holy Spirit is *not* merely a force, but a person. In John 16:7-11 we learn that He is the Advocate, that He is the one who convinces a person that they are a sinner, and that it is by faith in Christ that we can be made righteous.

The Holy Spirit then continues to play a vital role in the life of the believer.

• **From** Ephesians 1:13b-14a, what does the Holy Spirit do for the person who puts their faith in Jesus Christ?

• **From** Acts 1:8a, what does the believer receive from the Holy Spirit, and what does this enable the believer to do?

God is working in us to make us like Himself. What do you learn about the Holy Spirit's work in this area of the believer's life?

· Romans 5:5b

· Galatians 5:22-23a

God desires that we have a relationship with Him. Jesus Christ died for our sin so that we can have that relationship, but trusting Him to take away our sin is just the beginning. To have a deepening relationship, you have to grow to know and understand a person.

- **From** John 16:13-14, what does the Holy Spirit do for the believer?

- **Are** you beginning to know and understand God? That is the Holy Spirit working in you.

Today's Bible Reading

When you believed, you were marked in him with a seal, the promised Holy Spirit, who is a deposit guaranteeing our inheritance until the redemption of those who are God's possession…

— Ephesians 1:13b-14a

But you will receive power when the Holy Spirit comes on you; and you will be my witnesses…

— Acts 1:8a

God's love has been poured out into our hearts through the Holy Spirit, who has been given to us.

— Romans 5:5b

But the fruit of the Spirit is love, joy, peace, forbearance, kindness, goodness, faithfulness, gentleness and self-control.

— Galatians 5:22-23a

But when he, the Spirit of truth, comes, he will guide you into all the truth. He will not speak on his own; he will speak only what he hears, and he will tell you what is yet to come. He will glorify me because it is from me that he will receive what he will make known to you.

— John 16:13-14

Additional reading:
John 16:7-11
1 Corinthians 12:13a

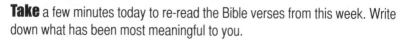

The Trinity - Day Seven

Take a few minutes today to re-read the Bible verses from this week. Write down what has been most meaningful to you.

We hope that you are knowing and understanding more about God, and that your relationship with Him is growing.

Lesson 4 — The Human Race

- We're a mess, or are we?
- Is there hope?

Remember, as you work through each daily lesson, pray and ask God to help you know, understand, and apply His truth to your life.

The Human Race - Day One

Read: Genesis 1:27 • Genesis 2:15 • Genesis 1:31a

Where did I come from? Why do so many bad things happen, and why is there so much evil in this world? Is there any hope? All these are legitimate questions, and God has provided the answers in His Word.

• **Read** Genesis 1:27 and answer the following:

  · Where did mankind (the human race) come from?

  · What genders are they?

  · In whose image are they made?

In Genesis we learn that God called the first man *Adam.* God then took one of Adam's ribs and created a woman, whom Adam named *Eve*.

• **From** Genesis 2:15, where did God place the man and what was he to do there?

God did not intend for people to be idle, but, as we will see, work at that time was not unpleasant toil.

- **What** did God say regarding His creation, including the man and the woman, in Genesis 1:31a?

As we look around our world, we see people doing evil and we see many things that are not good, such as sickness and death. We may wonder, "What happened?"

As we continue with our study we will discover that God has given us the answer, and He has given us hope.

Today's Bible Reading

So God created mankind in his own image, in the image of God he created them; male and female he created them.

— Genesis 1:27

The LORD God took the man and put him in the Garden of Eden to work it and take care of it.

— Genesis 2:15

God saw all that he had made, and it was very good.

— Genesis 1:31a

Additional reading:
Ecclesiastes 2:24
Genesis 2:7-25

The Human Race - Day Two

Read: Ezekiel 28:12b-17a • Isaiah 14:13-14

God does not reveal to us the origin of sin. However, many Bible scholars believe Ezekiel 28:12b-17a and Isaiah 14:12-17 refer to Satan[1] and reveal to us the first record of sin.

- **From** Ezekiel 28:12b-17a:

   · What was Satan like before "wickedness was found in" him?

   · Why did Satan become proud?

- **From** Isaiah 14:13-14, what did Satan say he would do?

---

[1]Satan is known by many different names, among them the devil, the serpent, Lucifer, and the deceiver.

In Isaiah 14:12,15 and Ezekiel 28:16-17 we learn of the evil one's expulsion from his heavenly position. In Revelation we read of his final judgment that is yet to take place. Of this being, who originally was so wonderfully created, Revelation 20:10 says, "The devil, who deceived them, was thrown into the lake of burning sulfur, where the beast and the false prophet had been thrown. They will be tormented day and night for ever and ever."

During the intervening time, he has caused great trouble for humanity, and will continue to wreak havoc right up to his final judgment.

Today's Bible Reading

You were the seal of perfection, full of wisdom and perfect in beauty. You were in Eden, the garden of God; every precious stone adorned you…Your settings and mountings were made of gold; on the day you were created they were prepared. You were anointed as a guardian cherub, for so I ordained you. You were on the holy mount of God; you walked among the fiery stones. You were blameless in your ways from the day you were created till wickedness was found in you. Through your widespread trade you were filled with violence, and you sinned. So I drove you in disgrace from the mount of God, and I expelled you, guardian cherub, from among the fiery stones. Your heart became proud on account of your beauty, and you corrupted your wisdom because of your splendor. So I threw you to the earth.

— Ezekiel 28:12b-17a

You said in your heart, "I will ascend to the heavens; I will raise my throne above the stars of God; I will sit enthroned on the mount of assembly, on the utmost heights of Mount Zaphon. I will ascend above the tops of the clouds; I will make myself like the Most High."

— Isaiah 14:13-14

Additional reading:
Isaiah 14:12, 15-17
Revelation 20:2a,10

The Human Race - Day Three

Read: Job 1:6-7 • Revelation 12:9 • 2 Corinthians 11:14 •
2 Corinthians 4:4 • John 8:44 • 1 Peter 5:8

Today we will learn a little more about our enemy, Satan, the evil one, who has created so many problems for the human race.

- **Unlike** God, Satan is a created being and is not omnipresent (present everywhere); however, he is not limited to hell. From Job 1:6-7, to what places does Satan have access?

- **The** serpent, Satan, is described as "crafty"[1] in Genesis 3:1. From the following verses, describe the character and activity of Satan.

  · Revelation 12:9

  · 2 Corinthians 11:14

  · 2 Corinthians 4:4

---

[1] According to the Oxford Dictionary, *crafty* means, "Clever at achieving one's aims by indirect or deceitful method."

· John 8:44

· 1 Peter 5:8

As you can see, our enemy is a powerful, crafty being. He has been deceiving the human race and leading people away from the truth for thousands of years.

Ephesians 2:2 tells us that he is "the spirit who is now at work in those who are disobedient." He does not want to be your friend—he wants to steal, kill, and destroy (see John 10:10)—but Jesus Christ came to destroy the devil's work (see 1 John 3:8b) and to give you an abundant life.

Today's Bible Reading

One day the angels came to present themselves before the Lord, and Satan also came with them. The Lord said to Satan, "Where have you come from?" Satan answered the Lord, "From roaming throughout the earth, going back and forth on it."

— Job 1:6-7

The great dragon was hurled down—that ancient serpent called the devil, or Satan, who leads the whole world astray. He was hurled to the earth, and his angels with him.

— Revelation 12:9

…Satan himself masquerades as an angel of light.

— 2 Corinthians 11:14

…has blinded the minds of unbelievers, so that they cannot see the light of the gospel that displays the glory of Christ…

— 2 Corinthians 4:4

He was a murderer…there is no truth in him…he is a liar and the father of lies.

— John 8:44

Your enemy the devil prowls around like a roaring lion looking for someone to devour.

— 1 Peter 5:8

Additional reading:
Genesis 3:1
Ephesians 2:1-2
John 10:10
1 John 3:8b

The Human Race - Day Four

Read: Genesis 2:16-17 • Genesis 3:1-6

As we previously learned, when God finished creating the world He saw that everything He had made was good, including Adam and Eve (the first people). And yet, when we look around our world, we see a creation filled with sin, sickness, death, and the accompanying sorrow and decay, and we ask, "What happened?"

• **What** command did God give to the man in Genesis 2:16-17? What would the consequences be for disobedience?

Adam and Eve were living in the Garden of Eden, a paradise. There was nothing unpleasant for them to experience, and they were free to enjoy everything. Only one command was given to them. Just think, only one rule.

• **Read** Genesis 3:1-6 and answer the following:

· How did the serpent (Satan) approach the woman—what question did he ask her?

· How did she reply?

· Satan contradicted what God said. What did Satan say would happen if she ate the fruit?

· Why did Eve take the fruit and eat it?

· After she ate it, whom did she give it to, and where was he?

Adam and Eve had a choice to make and act upon—whom would they believe? It was a simple choice. Believe God and His warning that eating the fruit would bring death, or believe Satan and his lie about the benefits of eating the fruit. We know that they chose to believe Satan because they ate the fruit.

We all have the same choice before us that they had: believe God or don't believe Him. Like Adam and Eve, we often think that God's rules are His attempt to withhold something good from us, rather than His warning to protect us from something that will harm us. And, like Adam and Eve, our choice is reflected in our actions.

· **Can** you think of choices you've made that you believed would bring you pleasure or good, but instead they have harmed you or brought you grief?

Today's Bible Reading

And the LORD God commanded the man, "You are free to eat from any tree in the garden; but you must not eat from the tree of the knowledge of good and evil, for when you eat from it you will surely die."
— Genesis 2:16-17

Now the serpent was more crafty than any of the wild animals the Lord God had made. He said to the woman, "Did God really say, 'You must not eat from any tree in the garden'?" The woman said to the serpent, "We may eat fruit from the trees in the garden, but God did say, 'You must not eat fruit from the tree that is in the middle of the garden, and you must not touch it, or you will die.'"

"You will not certainly die," the serpent said to the woman. "For God knows that when you eat from it your eyes will be opened, and you will be like God, knowing good and evil." When the woman saw that the fruit of the tree was good for food and pleasing to the eye, and also desirable for gaining wisdom, she took some and ate it. She also gave some to her husband, who was with her, and he ate it.
— Genesis 3:1-6

The Human Race - Day Five

Read: Genesis 3:12-13 • Genesis 3:16-19

Genesis 3:7-24 tells of the results of Adam and Eve's unbelief. Although they did not immediately die physically, the process of decay began that led to their eventual death.[1] Their disobedience (sin) did, however, bring about their immediate spiritual death (see Ephesians 2:1), and they hid from God.

But God knew where they were and what they had done, and He called them to account for it; nor did the serpent avoid God's judgment.

- **Read** Genesis 3:12-13 and Genesis 3:16-19 and answer the following:

  · When questioned by God, whom did the man blame for his disobedience?

  · Whom did the woman blame?

  · What was God's judgment on the woman?

---

[1] Adam died at the age of 930 years (Genesis 5:5)

· What was God's judgment on the man?

Today's Bible Reading

The man said, "The woman you put here with me--she gave me some fruit from the tree, and I ate it." Then the LORD God said to the woman, "What is this you have done?" The woman said, "The serpent deceived me, and I ate."

— Genesis 3:12-13

• **These** judgments that God placed on the human race are a constant reminder that we live in a fallen world. At every turn in life, God has placed His reminders to call us back to Himself. Have you turned from going your own way and turned to God? Won't you do it now?

To the woman he said, "I will make your pains in childbearing very severe; with painful labor you will give birth to children. Your desire will be for your husband, and he will rule over you." To Adam he said, "Because you listened to your wife and ate fruit from the tree about which I commanded you, 'You must not eat from it,' Cursed is the ground because of you; through painful toil you will eat food from it all the days of your life. It will produce thorns and thistles for you, and you will eat the plants of the field. By the sweat of your brow you will eat your food until you return to the ground, since from it you were taken; for dust you are and to dust you will return

— Genesis 3:16-19

Now we know what happened to creation. We see why sin, death, sickness, toil, sadness, sorrow, and suffering exist. You may think that God is unfair or harsh. As we continue our study, we will discover God's remedy and the hope He has given us.

Additional reading:
Genesis 3:7-24
Ephesians 2:1

The Human Race - Day Six

Read: Genesis 3:21 • Genesis 3:22-24

Prior to disobeying God, Adam and Eve had been naked and unashamed. After sinning, Adam and Eve made a futile attempt to cover their nakedness because they had become ashamed.

- **Read** Genesis 3:21 and answer the following:
  - What did God make for Adam and Eve?

  - What would have happened to an animal in order for its skin to become a covering for Adam and Eve?

God brought about the death of an animal in order to cover the nakedness caused by Adam and Eve's sin. This was the first physical death. Although it is mentioned here in just one sentence, in upcoming lessons we will see just how important this was and how it pictured the hope God would extend to the human race.

- **From** Genesis 3:22-24, what was God's concern, and what did He do about it?

Adam and Eve had known God, who is life. They had walked and talked with Him in the Garden. Now their sin had broken that relationship and had allowed sin and death (and all the accompanying sorrows) to enter God's perfect world.

- **In** mercy, God kept them from the tree of life. Write out what you think this fallen world would be like if there was no physical death to stop evil people and to end the suffering of sickness and disease in the physical body.

The LORD God made garments of skin for Adam and his wife and clothed them.

— Genesis 3:21

And the LORD God said, "The man has now become like one of us, knowing good and evil. He must not be allowed to reach out his hand and take also from the tree of life and eat, and live forever." So the LORD God banished him from the Garden of Eden to work the ground from which he had been taken. After he drove the man out, he placed on the east side of the Garden of Eden cherubim and a flaming sword flashing back and forth to guard the way to the tree of life.

— Genesis 3:22-24

The Human Race - Day Seven

Take a few minutes today to re-read the Bible verses from this week. Write down what has been most meaningful to you.

We hope you are learning to trust God, even when He says, "No."

Lesson 5 — Sin, Death, Life

· So what is sin, anyway?

· Why is there death?

· Is this as good as it gets?

Remember, as you work through each daily lesson, pray and ask God to help you know, understand, and apply His truth to your life.

Sin, Death, Life - Day One

Read: Ephesians 2:1 • Isaiah 59:2a • John 17:3 • Genesis 5:3a • Romans 5:12a

Death is separation. Physical death occurs when the body and the spirit are separated (see James 2:26a). Spiritual death occurs when the spirit is separated from God.

• **From** the following verses what do you learn about spiritual life (eternal life) and spiritual death?

   · Ephesians 2:1

   · Isaiah 59:2a[1]

   · John 17:3

Adam and Eve had known God, who is life. They had walked and talked with Him in the Garden, but their sin had broken that relationship. Although originally created in the image of God, they had become spiritually separated from Him—spiritually dead.

• **What** do you learn about Adam's offspring in Genesis 5:3a?

---

[1] According to the Merriam Webster Online Dictionary, *iniquity* means, "wicked act or thing: sin."

· **What** does Romans 5:12 tell us that may help you understand why sin and death affect all people?

Adam's offspring were born with his fallen nature. Every human since has been born with that same nature, since we have all descended from Adam. We sin because we are born with this fallen, sinful nature (see Ephesians 2:2-3). You don't have to teach a child to do wrong; they do it by nature. The long history of our planet demonstrates that where the human race goes, evil springs up.

Again we see that it is God's grace and mercy that stopped humanity from living forever in this fallen state. He has also given us a future and a hope. He has made a way to restore to us what was lost because of Adam and Eve's sin. As we continue with our study, we will see what great lengths God has gone to and the great love He has shown toward all people.

Today's Bible Reading

As for you, you were dead in your transgressions and sins.
— Ephesians 2:1

But your iniquities have separated you from your God…
— Isaiah 59:2a

Now this is eternal life: that they know you, the only true God, and Jesus Christ, whom you have sent.
— John 17:3

When Adam had lived 130 years, he had a son in his own likeness, in his own image…
— Genesis 5:3a

Therefore, just as sin entered the world through one man, and death through sin, and in this way death came to all people, because all sinned…
— Romans 5:12

Additional reading:
James 2:26a
Ephesians 2:2-3
Ephesians 4:18

Sin, Death, Life - Day Two

Read: Romans 3:10-12 • Romans 8:7-8 • Isaiah 53:6a • Romans 3:23

Human beings sin because they are born with a sin nature, Adam's fallen nature.

• **What** does Romans 3:10-12 say regarding this?

• **What** do you learn about this sinful nature from Romans 8:7-8?

• **What** does Isaiah 53:6a say about each one of us?

Have you considered this before? We were created by and for God, and He knows what will fulfill us, yet we each go our own way, doing our own "thing."

• **What** does Romans 3:23 say regarding each of us?

Are you the person you want to be? Do you believe you have lived up to your full potential? Have you ever let yourself down? Have you honestly lived up to your own standards? Since we don't even do that, how much less do we live up to God's perfect standard—His glory—which is nothing less than perfection?

You may say, "But, nobody is perfect." And that is the point. Although we were originally made in God's image, all of us fall short of perfection. We are all born with that fallen, less than perfect, sinful nature.

At any time God could have wiped us all out and started all over again, but He loved us and has made the way for us to be made perfect and to have a relationship with Himself.

Today's Bible Reading

As it is written: "There is no one righteous, not even one; there is no one who understands, no one who seeks God. All have turned away, they have together become worthless; there is no one who does good, not even one."

— Romans 3:10-12

The mind governed by the flesh is hostile to God; it does not submit to God's law, nor can it do so. Those who are in the realm of the flesh cannot please God.

— Romans 8:7-8

We all, like sheep, have gone astray, each of us has turned to our own way…

— Isaiah 53:6a

…for all have sinned and fall short of the glory of God.

— Romans 3:23

Sin, Death, Life - Day Three

Read: Hebrews 9:22b • Hebrews 10:4

Let us review some of what we have learned:

- God is perfect and holy.
- He created the first two humans (Adam and Eve) in His image, and initially they were perfect.
- God gave Adam and Eve one rule: don't eat the fruit of the tree of the knowledge of good and evil. If you do, you will die.
- Rather than believing God, they believed the serpent (Satan) when he said that God was withholding something good from them, and that if they ate the fruit they wouldn't die, but instead they would be like God.
- Their unbelief led them to eat the fruit.
- They immediately died spiritually, and eventually they died physically.
- All of their offspring were then born spiritually dead and with a nature determined to sin. Each of these offspring, too, has the sentence of physical death (see Hebrews 9:27).
- God loves the human race (the offspring of Adam and Eve), and wants to restore to them what was lost through sin and unbelief.

In Genesis 3 we read that God killed an animal to cover the result of Adam and Eve's sin.

- **What** does Hebrews 9:22b tell you about forgiveness?

- **From** Hebrews 10:4, what do you learn about the blood of animal sacrifices?

These animals were a temporary substitute. The blood of these animals covered sin and made a way for people to enter a relationship with God (see Psalm 32:1 and Psalm 85:2b), but it was unable to take away the sin.

Animal sacrifices, along with other Jewish religious practices, were merely "shadows" of what God was going to do for humanity (see Colossians 2:17).[1]

- **Are** you beginning to see and understand the seriousness of sin—all sin?

Today's Bible Reading

...and without the shedding of blood there is no forgiveness.

— Hebrews 9:22b

It is impossible for the blood of bulls and goats to take away sins.

— Hebrews 10:4

Additional reading:
Hebrews 9:27
Psalm 32:1
Psalm 85:2b
Colossians 2:17

---

[1] God has done away with these animal sacrifices and made a new and better way, which we will learn about in our next lesson.

Sin, Death, Life - Day Four

Read: Exodus 12:13 • John 1:29 • 1 Corinthians 5:7b • 1 John 1:7b

Immediately after Adam and Eve sinned, God established the blood sacrifice as the means for people to have their sin covered, in order for them to come into a relationship with Him (see Genesis 4:3-4; Hebrews 11:4). People then had a choice: believe what God said and come to Him by way of the blood sacrifice, or don't believe Him and don't come into relationship with Him.

Throughout the Old Testament, by faith (believing what God said), godly people came into relationship with God through the blood of the animal sacrifice—Abel, Noah, Abraham, Isaac, Jacob, etc. (See Additional Reading.)

Exodus 12 tells how God forced the Egyptian Pharaoh to let God's people (Israel) go free after 400 years of enslavement. The Israelites were to kill a lamb and place some of the blood on the sides and tops of the doorframes of their houses. The Lord would then pass throughout Egypt and strike down every firstborn of those who were not marked with the blood, in order to bring judgment on the gods of Egypt.

- **From** Exodus 12:13, what purpose would the blood of the lamb serve for the people of Israel who believed and obeyed God's instructions?

These sacrifices were but shadows or pictures of what Jesus Christ would do on our behalf.

- **What** did John the Baptist say about Jesus Christ in John 1:29?

Jesus is our sacrifice. His blood doesn't just cover our sin, it takes away our sin. Just as God provided an animal sacrifice to cover the results of

Adam and Eve's sin, He has provided the perfect sacrifice to not merely cover, but to take away our sin.

- **What** do the following verses say about this?

  · 1 Corinthians 5:7b

  · 1 John 1:7b

Perhaps this is the first time you have really understood that Jesus Christ is the sacrifice for your sin—that His blood takes away sin. You have a choice: whether or not to believe God. God sent His Son, Jesus Christ, to be the Savior, the sacrifice, for the world (see 1 John 4:14, Romans 3:25). Until Jesus Christ died, people came into relationship with God through the sacrifice of an animal to cover their sin; now we come into relationship with God by way of the Lamb of God (Jesus), who takes away our sin.

It is simple...believe God. It is not by your works or your deeds that your sin is forgiven; it is by believing Him—this is faith. It is not by the sacrifice of Jesus *plus* your deeds; it is *only* by putting your faith in Jesus, in His sacrifice, to take away your sin.

- **If** you have never done this, won't you do it now? Just trust that what God said is true, that Jesus paid the price for your sin, and tell Him, "Thank You."

Today's Bible Reading

The blood will be a sign for you on the houses where you are; and when I see the blood, I will pass over you. No destructive plague will touch you when I strike Egypt.

— Exodus 12:13

The next day John saw Jesus coming toward him and said, "Look, the Lamb of God, who takes away the sin of the world!"

— John 1:29

...For Christ, our Passover lamb, has been sacrificed.

— 1 Corinthians 5:7b

...the blood of Jesus, his Son, purifies us from all sin.

— 1 John 1:7b

Additional reading:
Genesis 4:3-7
Hebrews 11:4
Genesis 8:20
Genesis 12:8
Genesis 26:25
Genesis 35:7
1 John 4:14
Romans 3:25
John 14:6

Sin, Death, Life - Day Five

Read: 2 Corinthians 5:21 • 1 Peter 3:18a • 1 Corinthians 15:3-4 •
Revelation 5:12-13 • Revelation 5:9b-10

The sacrifice of Jesus Christ for our sin was God's plan from the beginning
(see Revelation 13:8b). Only Jesus Christ could pay the price for our sin.
Remember, the wage for sin is death (see Romans 6:23). No matter how
much a person loves another person, it would be impossible for them to die
to pay the price for the other's sin, because they have to die for their own
sin. So let us consider how Jesus could do this.

- As we learned, we are born sinners because the sin nature has been
passed down to us from Adam.

- Although Jesus Christ was born as a human from Mary, he did not have
a human father. The Holy Spirit moved on Mary and the child that was
born of her was the perfect Son of God.

- **What** do the following verses say about Jesus Christ?

- 2 Corinthians 5:21

- 1 Peter 3:18a

- 1 Corinthians 15:3-4

As we look into the future in Revelation, we see the risen Lord Jesus Christ, the Lamb of God, seated on the throne.

- **Describe** what is happening in Revelation 5:12-13.

- **In** Revelation we learn many things about the Lamb of God. From Revelation 5:9b-10 why are they praising Him—what did He accomplish?

Take a moment right now and tell Jesus how grateful you are for all that He has accomplished on your behalf.

Today's Bible Reading

God made him who had no sin to be sin for us, so that in him we might become the righteousness of God.
—2 Corinthians 5:21

For Christ also suffered once for sins, the righteous for the unrighteous, to bring you to God.
— 1 Peter 3:18a

For what I received I passed on to you as of first importance: that Christ died for our sins according to the Scriptures, that he was buried, that he was raised on the third day according to the Scriptures…
1 Corinthians 15:3-4

In a loud voice they were saying: "Worthy is the Lamb, who was slain, to receive power and wealth and wisdom and strength and honor and glory and praise!" Then I heard every creature in heaven and on earth and under the earth and on the sea, and all that is in them, saying: "To him who sits on the throne and to the Lamb be praise and honor and glory and power, for ever and ever."
— Revelation 5:12-13

…because you were slain, and with your blood you purchased for God persons from every tribe and language and people and nation. You have made them to be a kingdom and priests to serve our God, and they will reign on the earth.
Revelation 5:9b-10

Additional reading:
Revelation 13:8b
Romans 6:23

Sin, Death, Life - Day Six

Read: Revelation 21:1-6a • 1 Corinthians 2:9

God weaves His story of redemption from the first book of the Bible, Genesis, to the last book, Revelation. The Old Testament (Genesis-Malachi) tells of God's creation, humanity's fall, and the promise of the Savior who would come.

The New Testament (Matthew-Revelation) tells of the Savior, Jesus Christ, what He accomplished, is accomplishing, and will yet accomplish.

He tells us His story in different ways, using different examples, as He teaches us about all He has done and will do on our behalf.

Revelation was written by the Apostle John toward the end of his life. In it we see a glimpse into the future and on into eternity.

• **Read** Revelation 21:1-6a and answer the following:

· What does John see?

· Where will God dwell?

· What will not be there?

· What will be made new?

· **These** words are hints of the wonderful things God has planned for those who love Him. What does 1 Corinthians 2:9 tell us about what He has planned?

Today's Bible Reading

Then I saw "a new heaven and a new earth," for the first heaven and the first earth had passed away, and there was no longer any sea. I saw the Holy City, the new Jerusalem, coming down out of heaven from God, prepared as a bride beautifully dressed for her husband. And I heard a loud voice from the throne saying, "Look! God's dwelling place is now among the people, and he will dwell with them. They will be his people, and God himself will be with them and be their God. 'He will wipe every tear from their eyes. There will be no more death or mourning or crying or pain, for the old order of things has passed away."
He who was seated on the throne said, "I am making everything new!" Then he said, "Write this down, for these words are trustworthy and true." He said to me: "It is done. I am the Alpha and the Omega, the Beginning and the End."

— Revelation 21:1-6a

However, as it is written: "What no eye has seen, what no ear has heard, and what no human mind has conceived"—the things God has prepared for those who love him…

— 1 Corinthians 2:9

Sin, Death, Life - Day Seven

Take a few minutes today to re-read the Bible verses from this week. Write down what has been most meaningful to you.

We hope you have accepted Jesus Christ as your Savior, the sacrifice for your sin, and are looking forward to all that God has planned for you. (See page 4 for additional information about this.)

Lesson 6 — Knowing

- Life is difficult!
- Is there hope, a future?

Remember, as you work through each daily lesson, pray and ask God to help you know, understand, and apply His truth to your life.

Knowing - Day One

Read: 2 Peter 3:10,12b-13 • 2 Peter 3:8-9

People often ask why God doesn't do something right now about the evil in the world. As we have learned, evil entered the world when Satan tempted Eve, and she and her husband, Adam, directly disobeyed God. This tendency to evil—to sin—has permeated the human race. Whatever is good, we eventually manage to pervert it. We have even turned God's law, which is good (see 1 Timothy 1:8), into legalism, and use it in a manner that God did not intend.

All the misery in this world is caused directly or indirectly by humanity's sin. Some misery is caused by a person's own sin, some is caused by another's sin, and some is the result of Adam's sin and what it has done to God's perfect creation.

In previous lessons, we have seen how sin spreads like a cancer. We saw it first in the heart of Satan, then his angels, then Eve, Adam, and all of the human race. The only thing that can be done for sin is to get rid of it completely, as surely as you have to get rid of all cancer cells in a body or the cancer will begin to spread and destroy once again.

- **From** 2 Peter 3:10,12b-13, what is God going to do one day in the future?

- **Knowing** how sin spreads and the destruction that it brings, what do you think would happen to this new heaven and earth if God allowed sin to enter it?

When God makes all things new, He will not allow sin to enter. It will be the home of righteousness, with all the accompanying peace and joy. If God allowed sin to enter, then the evil and the misery it brings would begin all over again. This would not be love, and God is love.

Remember, He has provided the way, through Jesus Christ, for our sin to be removed so that we can be with Him forever, sharing in this new creation.

- **Read** 2 Peter 3:8-9 and answer the following:

  · Why hasn't God fulfilled His promise to end the misery in this world?

  · Will you thank Him for waiting for you? Are there those you don't want to see perish? Share with them God's glorious good news and pray that God's Spirit will convict them of sin and stir a hunger in their heart for His truth.

Today's Bible Reading

But the day of the Lord will come like a thief. The heavens will disappear with a roar; the elements will be destroyed by fire, and the earth and everything done in it will be laid bare…That day will bring about the destruction of the heavens by fire, and the elements will melt in the heat. But in keeping with his promise we are looking forward to a new heaven and a new earth, where righteousness dwells.

— 2 Peter 3:10,12b-13

But do not forget this one thing, dear friends: With the Lord a day is like a thousand years, and a thousand years are like a day. The Lord is not slow in keeping his promise, as some understand slowness. Instead he is patient with you, not wanting anyone to perish, but everyone to come to repentance.

— 2 Peter 3:8-9

Additional reading:
1 Timothy 1:8

Knowing - Day Two

Read: Galatians 5:22-23a • Ephesians 5:9

God knows we can't get rid of our own sin. That is why He tells us to come to Him just as we are, but thankfully He doesn't leave us just as we are. He forgives and cleanses us, and begins working in us to make us like Jesus (see 2 Corinthians 3:18). In Romans 8:28-29 He tells us that, for those who love Him, He is working everything together for good to make us like His Son.

This change comes from His life in us and flowing through us, and is sometimes referred to as bearing "fruit" (see John 15:4-6).

- **Describe** this fruit from the following verses:

  · Galatians 5:22-23a

  · Ephesians 5:9

- **Perhaps** when you first read these verses it doesn't seem like a "big deal," but consider the opposite of several of the fruit of the Spirit. According Merriam Webster's Online Dictionary:

  · The opposite of "love" is animosity, antagonism, antipathy, aversion, disfavor, dislike, enmity, hostility, abhorrence, disgust, repugnance, repulsion, and revulsion.

  · The opposite of "joy" is misery, sadness, unhappiness, and wretchedness.

· The opposite of "peace" is nervousness, fear, fearfulness, torment, upset, doubt, dread, foreboding, strife, trouble, tumult, turmoil, unrest, upheaval, and fighting.

• **Which** do you want in your life—the fruit of the Spirit or its opposite? Are you thankful that God doesn't leave us as we are, but begins to change us so that we produce this fruit, this Christ-likeness?

Remember, fruit doesn't grow all at once. It takes time (see Mark 4:28), but God is the gardener (see John 15:1), and He is the one working in us (see Philippians 2:13). With this knowledge we can settle down, put our faith in our Heavenly Father, and trust that He is working all things together for good to make us like His Son.

Today's Bible Reading

But the fruit of the Spirit is love, joy, peace, forbearance, kindness, goodness, faithfulness, gentleness and self-control.

Galatians 5:22-23a

For the fruit of the light consists in all goodness, righteousness and truth.

Ephesians 5:9

Additional reading:
2 Corinthians 3:18
Romans 8:28-29
John 15:4-6
Mark 4:28
John 15:1
Philippians 2:13

Knowing - Day Three

Read: Hebrews 12:10-11

In our last lesson the Bible compared us to a plant bearing fruit to explain how God works in the lives of those who have put their faith in Him, to make them like His Son. In today's example God uses the relationship of a father and child.

In Hebrews 12 we are told that if we are God's child, He will most certainly discipline us. Answer the following questions from Hebrews 12:10-11.

- **What** is the purpose of God's discipline?

- **Is** the discipline pleasant at the time?

- **What** will be the result of the discipline in the life of those who are trained by it?[1]

---

[1] Righteousness and peace are descriptions of Jesus Christ.

Consider the different types of discipline a parent may exercise over a child:

- If a child is learning to play an instrument, they may have to learn the discipline of practicing for a certain length of time daily.
- If a youth wants to play a sport, they may have to learn the discipline of doing certain exercises and eating a strict diet on a daily basis.
- If a child has misbehaved or not followed the rules, there may be a verbal rebuke.
- If the behavior persists, the child may have some of their privileges restricted or some other type of negative consequence.
- Finally, in some cultures, there may be physical discipline.

God deals with us in the same manner. Even though it may not be enjoyable for the moment, we know that God is dealing with us as His children and that we will benefit by His discipline, both now and throughout eternity.

Today's Bible Reading

[Our human fathers] disciplined us for a little while as they thought best; but God disciplines us for our good, in order that we may share in his holiness. No discipline seems pleasant at the time, but painful. Later on, however, it produces a harvest of righteousness and peace for those who have been trained by it.

— Hebrews 12:10-11

Additional reading:
1 Timothy 4:8

Knowing - Day Four

Read: Isaiah 48:10 • 1 Peter 1:6-7 • James 1:2-4 • 1 Thessalonians 5:18

Another example we are given of how God works in us is that of a refiner of precious metal, such as silver or gold. The refiner takes the unrefined metal and heats it until it liquefies. The impurities, or dross, rise to the top and are scooped off, leaving only the pure silver or gold. God is the refiner, and we are the precious metal that has not yet been refined.

• **From** Isaiah 48:10, what is one way God refines us?

First Peter chapter 1 speaks of all that God has for us in the future, of how we are shielded by faith, and that we greatly rejoice because of this. It also speaks of our current trials and difficulties.

• **What** do you learn about trials from 1 Peter 1:6-7?

• **James** chapter 1 also speaks of trials, their purpose, and our response to them. Read James 1:2-4 and answer the following:

· How should the Christian view trials?

· What purpose do trials serve in the Christian's life?

When a person is content, filled with peace and joy, truly knowing God, understanding what is transpiring in their life, and looking forward to a glorious future, they can face the difficulties of life with confidence.

- **Do** you really want all that God has for you? Do you really want Him to work in and through you?

If your answer is yes, you can count trials as joy, even if you don't like the trial. (If you liked it, it wouldn't be a trial.)

- **What** instruction do you receive in 1 Thessalonians 5:18?

As you see, God has placed a choice before you: Do you really trust Him? Do you believe that God truly has your best interest at heart? Consider the difficulties you are facing at this moment. They may have come through no fault of your own.

- **Will** you trust that He is working all these things together for your good (not necessarily the way you think it should be, but for your good), to make you like Jesus? Will you trust Him to work everything out according to His will and purpose?

If you do, take a moment now and thank Him for who He is and what He is doing in your life.

Today's Bible Reading

See, I have refined you, though not as silver; I have tested you in the furnace of affliction.
— Isaiah 48:10

In all this you greatly rejoice, though now for a little while you may have had to suffer grief in all kinds of trials. These have come so that the proven genuineness of your faith—of greater worth than gold, which perishes even though refined by fire —may result in praise, glory and honor when Jesus Christ is revealed.
— 1 Peter 1:6-7

Consider it pure joy, my brothers and sisters, whenever you face trials of many kinds, because you know that the testing of your faith produces perseverance. Let perseverance finish its work so that you may be mature and complete, not lacking anything.
— James 1:2-4

Give thanks in all circumstances, for this is God's will for you in Christ Jesus.
— 1 Thessalonians 5:18

Additional reading:
Psalm 66:10
Proverbs 17:3

Knowing - Day Five

Read: Ephesians 6:10-18a

God is working everything for our good. However, we still need to be aware that a battle is going on.

Read Ephesians 6:10-18a, and answer the following questions:

- **Who** is our struggle against?

- **Whose** strength do we rely on?

- **Why** are we to put on the armor of God?

Our strength is His strength. We need not fear our weakness. In 2 Corinthians 12:9 God says, "My grace is sufficient for you, for my power is made perfect in weakness."

After putting on God's armor, all we need to do is take our stand, stand our ground, and pray. The enemy will shoot flaming arrows at us, attempting to distract us, to cause us to doubt God, and to discourage us from praying.

- **From** today's verses, what extinguishes those flaming arrows?

The evil one, the enemy of our soul, uses the same tactic on us that he used on Adam and Eve. He wants us to doubt God—His love, His wisdom, His power, His goodness. And like them, we have a choice—believe who God says He is and what He has said, or don't. That is the shield of faith! We don't have to understand just how God is working, or why He allows something. We just have to trust that:

- He is all-powerful.
- He is all-knowing.
- He is all-wise.
- He is completely good.
- He is love. (He knows and loves each of us intimately, and is working all things together for our good and His glory.[1])

When we doubt any of these, we often fail to pray, and instead of standing our ground, we may stumble. But even then, God has promised that if we fall, He will lift us up (see Proverbs 24:16 and Psalm 145:14).

- **Is** there some trial or difficulty you are facing, and is the enemy telling you that God doesn't care or that the situation can never be worked for good? If you are discouraged and doubt has filled your mind, you may want to pray the prayer of the man in Mark 9:24, "I do believe; help me overcome my unbelief!"

---

[1]When we bear the fruit of the Spirit, it brings the Father glory (see John 15:8).

Today's Bible Reading

Finally, be strong in the Lord and in his mighty power. Put on the full armor of God, so that you can take your stand against the devil's schemes. For our struggle is not against flesh and blood, but against the rulers, against the authorities, against the powers of this dark world and against the spiritual forces of evil in the heavenly realms. Therefore put on the full armor of God, so that when the day of evil comes, you may be able to stand your ground, and after you have done everything, to stand.

Stand firm then, with the belt of truth buckled around your waist, with the breastplate of righteousness in place, and with your feet fitted with the readiness that comes from the gospel of peace. In addition to all this, take up the shield of faith, with which you can extinguish all the flaming arrows of the evil one. Take the helmet of salvation and the sword of the Spirit, which is the word of God. And pray in the Spirit on all occasions with all kinds of prayers and requests.

—Ephesians 6:10-18a

Additional reading:
2 Corinthians 12:9
Proverbs 24:16
Psalm 145:14
Mark 9:24

Knowing - Day Six

Read: Romans 8:31b-32 • Romans 8:33-34 • Romans 8:38-39 •
Jeremiah 29:11-13

As we come to the end of this study, we hope that we have helped answer some of the "Why?" questions of this life, and that you have come to understand just how great is God's love for you.

• **From** Romans 8:31b-32, how do we know that there is nothing that can succeed against God's glorious plan for us?

• **From** Romans 8:33-34, why can no charge that is brought against us stand, and why will we not be condemned for any wrong we have done and any good we have failed to do?

In all the possible difficulties and troubles that life can throw our way, we don't just conquer, we are greater than conquerors, because God works it all for our good and for His glory. Everything—joys and sorrows, easy times and trials—benefits us now and throughout eternity (see Romans 8:18 and Romans 8:35-37).

- **From** Romans 8:38-39, what are some of the things that cannot separate us from the love of God that is in Christ Jesus our Lord?

In the midst of this fallen world, with all its sorrows and difficulties, we can live lives filled with love, peace, and joy. We can live with confidence that God knows what is transpiring in our lives, and that He has it under control, working it all together for our good and His glory.

- **What** promises has He given in Jeremiah 29:11-13?

Today's Bible Reading

...If God is for us, who can be against us? He who did not spare his own Son, but gave him up for us all--how will he not also, along with him, graciously give us all things?

— Romans 8:31b-32

Who will bring any charge against those whom God has chosen? It is God who justifies. Who then is the one who condemns? No one. Christ Jesus who died—more than that, who was raised to life—is at the right hand of God and is also interceding for us.

— Romans 8:33-34

For I am convinced that neither death nor life, neither angels nor demons, neither the present nor the future, nor any powers, neither height nor depth, nor anything else in all creation, will be able to separate us from the love of God that is in Christ Jesus our Lord.

— Romans 8:38-39

"For I know the plans I have for you," declares the Lord, "plans to prosper you and not to harm you, plans to give you hope and a future. Then you will call on me and come and pray to me, and I will listen to you. You will seek me and find me when you seek me with all your heart."

— Jeremiah 29:11-13

Additional reading:
Romans 8:18
Romans 8:35-37

Knowing - Day Seven

Take a few minutes today to re-read the Bible verses from this week. Write down what has been most meaningful to you.

Because God is infinite and His Word is living, you can spend the rest of your life growing to know Him better as you study His Word. If you have accepted Jesus Christ as your Savior—as the sacrifice for your sin—then you have become a child of God and have just started on this wonderful journey of knowing God. *Joy of Living* has many studies that will help you on your journey.